# One Day Means A Lot

# One Day Means A Lot

### by

## MARISA (Pseud.)

*marisa Lonette*

## PICTURES BY REISIE LONETTE

THE BOBBS-MERRILL COMPANY, INC.

A SUBSIDIARY OF HOWARD W. SAMS & CO., INC.

PUBLISHERS   INDIANAPOLIS   KANSAS CITY   NEW YORK

*For Vincent –*
*and the little white horse*

Bird, come to me
Bring me the sky
Lend me your wings
So I can
Fly.

One day means a lot
And one day comes
And comes again
And doesn't mean as much.

When Spring comes
All the children are happy.
All except one—
Mary—she is shy.

Jack-in-the-box
Comes out of his box
And calls for his friends
Each·day.
He smiles
Shows them his tricks
He waves
And then goes away.

The cat winked at me

I winked back

He winked twice

He is black

And has yellow eyes.

No matter how far you run
And skip and hop
You can never run away
From the sky.

Sunshine, sunshine
Come wake us up
Then go wake the trees.

Come back again
We have a present
For you.

A little cloud on top of me
Opened—
And the sun shined down
On me.

Little white horse
Run away—
You are made of silk and cotton.
Run away to a lovely place
Where no one is there but you
So you can have freedom.

*To a Lollypop*

Beautiful thing
Beautiful thing
How can I lick you away?
How can I
Lick
You
Away
?

When I grow up I will be a m
I will own twenty children
I will have a wife named Mary

I know there is a fairy
Some place or other.
I think she is hiding
Under a leaf.
She wears a long gown
With splendid roses
Splendid slippers
And a crown.

We lived in a little doll house
On the beach
With silver cups and silver dishes.
A mermaid sang
And sea gulls screeched
Across the sky.

I saw a little sailboat
With the prettiest sails
I ever saw.
And I came running
Down the path.

I have a friend
His name is Harry
And he lives in a buttercup.
I visit him every day.
When I visit him
I listen to the birds
Sing to me.

Rosebush, so pretty as you are,
You surprised me—
All winter you were sleeping.
Today you woke up
Dressed in pink.

A fish named Sun Star
Swimming in the sea
Was captured by my brother,
Put into a glass bowl
With a stone
Of my own.

Poor Maureen on the beach

Lying on a rock—

Do you think a whale has swallowed her?

Or do you think

She is still

Lying on the beach?

Once I saw a little boy
Holding up a cake.
In the cake were candles
Lighted—
Singing each to each.

We danced and danced
Until the edge of the moon went dark,
As the train moved and moved
Still waving on.
And then it ended
And it was dark.

Have you met my Elizabeth?
My Lizzy, my Liz, my love?
She has white spots
On a big brown spot,
A chocolate nose
And a candy-cane tail.

I found my pumpkin in a field
With forty other pumpkins growing there.
I picked my pumpkin
And brought it home with me
To make a happy jack-o'-lantern
All lit up
For a special time.

I have wished on a star
I have wished on the sun
For a nice thing to happen.
When pumpkins laugh
When cows speak
And do not say moo—
O then will it happen?

Look up to the cuckoo bird
You will have beautiful thoughts,
Have beautiful dreams.

At night
When the forest is dark—
I walk with Carlotta and James—
The fireflies light the way.